**Ransom Neutron Stars**
Not Pop, Not Rock
by Helen Harvey
Illustrated by Kate Miller

Published by Ransom Publishing Ltd.
Unit 7, Brocklands Farm, West Meon, Hampshire GU32 1JN, UK
**www.ransom.co.uk**

ISBN 978 178591 423 2
First published in 2017
Reprinted 2018



A CIP catalogue record of this book is available from the British Library.

# Not Pop, Not Rock

Helen Harvey

Illustrated by Kate Miller

Kim, is it pop?

Sam,
get off!
*Tip tock,
tip tip tock.*

I bet it is dull.

No.

I bet it is sad.

It is not!

Is it a hit, Kim?

No.

Bip bip bop.
Bip bip bop.

Is it in the top ten?

No, Sam.
Bog off!

I bet it is rock.

Sam! A bit less fuss!
Boss! Tell him off!

On the bus . . .

*Pip tick, pip tock.*
*Pip tick, pip tock.*
No, Sam. It is not bad.

It is not bad,
not sad . . .

. . . not pop,
not rock . . .

But Kim,
I am a big fan
of bad pop.

Huh!
I am not!

SAM!

Can I?
I cannot
mess it up.

Let go, Sam.

No, I got it!

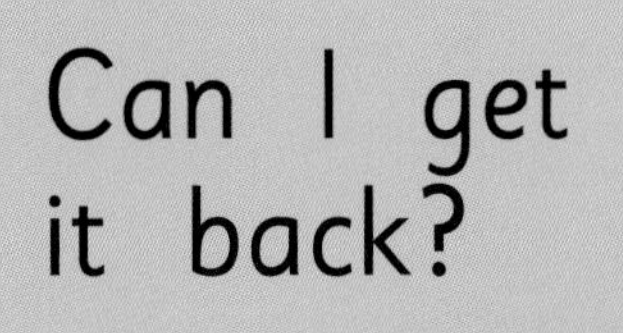
Can I get it back?

It’s hot!

Ts ts ts BAM!
Ts ts ts BAM!

Kim! It's hip hop! It is not pop and it is not rock. It is hip hop!

# Have you read?

**Go to the Laptop Man**

by Jill Atkins

**Gus and the Tin of Ham**

by Jill Atkins

# Have you read?

**Deep in the Dark Woods**

by Cath Jones

**Night Combat**

by Stephen Rickard

**Not Pop, Not Rock**
Word count **149**

Covers:
Letters and Sounds Phase 2

## Phonics

| | | | |
|---|---|---|---|
| *Phonics 1* | **Not Pop, Not Rock**<br>Go to the Laptop Man<br>Gus and the Tin of Ham | *Phonics 2* | Deep in the Dark Woods<br>Night Combat<br>Ben's Jerk Chicken Van |
| *Phonics 3* | GBH<br>Steel Pan Traffic Jam<br>Platform 7 | *Phonics 4* | The Rock Show<br>Gaps in the Brain<br>New Kinds of Energy |

## Book bands

| | | | |
|---|---|---|---|
| *Pink* | Curry!<br>Free Runners<br>My Toys | *Red* | Shopping with Zombies<br>Into the Scanner<br>Planting My Garden |
| *Yellow* | Fit for Love<br>The Lottery Ticket<br>In the Stars | *Blue* | Awesome ATAs<br>Wolves<br>The Giant Jigsaw |
| *Green* | Fly, May FLY!<br>How to Start Your Own Crazy Cult<br>The Care Home | *Orange* | Text Me<br>The Last Soldier<br>Best Friends |